Lindsay's
Chemical
Cross
Reference
Second Edition

Lindsay Publications Inc.
Bradley IL 60915

Lindsay's
Chemical
Cross-Reference
Second Edition

Paper: ISBN 1-55918-017-X

2 3 4 5 6 7 8 9 0

Introduction

This chemical cross-reference has been compiled by extracting information from chemistry textbooks, industrial references, and chemical formularies back to the early 1800's. Equivalents, definitions, and cross-reference entries were loaded into our computer, sorted into alphabetical order, and then merged into one master cross-reference which follows. You will find that capital letters have been eliminated to improve the purity of the alphabetization. You will also find a variety of spellings and definitions, many of which are contradictory. These variations and unusual terms have been retained to improve the historical usefulness of this cross reference.

WARNING!

Lindsay Publications Inc has compiled into one listing chemical definitions from many sources. There are probable spelling errors, and possibly, incorrect definitions which existed in the original editions and are repeated here. Slight differences in the spellings of chemical names can indicate quite different chemical compounds. Errors in the following listing, both those known and unknown, could cause users to formulate dangerous compounds by using incorrect reagents.

Many of the chemicals listed are extremely toxic and dangerous. No attempt has been made to differentiate between dangerous and safe chemicals. Unless you have knowledge to the contrary, you should assume that all chemicals are dangerous.

Lindsay Publications Inc claims no responsibility for the accuracy of the listing that follows, nor problems that these errors might cause. This cross-reference is provided to help understand archaic chemical terms found in arcane chemical texts and is not intended to be used as a chemical formulary or dictionary for laboratory workers.

Chemical Cross-Reference

absinthium, absinthe ....wormwood (distillate of)
acacia.. gum arabic
acetaldehyde .... acetic aldehyde, ethanol
acetamide................................... acetic acid amide & ethanamide
acetanilide................................... antifebrin and phenylacetamide
acetate .... salt of acetic acid
acetate of lime .... calcium acetate
acetic acid .... acid of vinegar, ethanoic acid
acetic acid amide .... acetamide
acetic anhydride .... acetic oxide
acetic ether .... ethylacetate
acetin .... glyceryl monoacetate
acetous salts .... acetates
acetum ....vinegar
acetum opii .... vinegar of opium
acetum scillae .... vinegar of squill
acetyl salicylic acid .... aspirin
acetylene .... ethine
acetylene tetrachloride............ acetosol, boroform,tetrachlorethane
acetylsalcylic acid .... aspirin, acetophen
acid of sulphur .... sulphuric acid
acid of vitrolic .... sulphuric acid
acid black...black acid type of dye
acid of aerial .... carbonic acid
acid of alum .... sulphuric acid
acid of amber .... succinic acid
acid of ants .... formic acid
acid of apples .... malic acid
acid of arsenic .... arsenic acid
acid of benzoin .... benzoic acid
acid of borax .... boracic acid
acid of calcareous .... carbonic acid
acid of chalk.. carbonic acid
acid of charcoal .... carbonic acid
acid of cork .... suberic acid
acid of cream of tartar .... tartaric acid
acid of cretaceous .... carbonic acid
acid of fat .... sebacic acid
acid of fluor ....fluoric acid
acid of galls .... gallic acid
acid of lac .... laccic acid
acid of lemons ....citric acid
acid of mephitic .... carbonic acid
acid of milk .... lactic acid

acid of molybdina .... molybdic acid
acid of nitre, dephlogisticated .... nitric acid
acid of nitre, phlogisticated .... nitrous acid
acid of phosphorus, dephlogisticated .... phosphoric acid
acid of phosphorus, phlogisticated .... phosphorus acid
acid of saccharine .... oxalic acid
acid of saccholactic .... mucous acid
acid of saltpetre, sea-salt, marine .... muriatic acid
acid of sedative .... boracic acid
acid of silk worms .... bombic acid
acid of spar .... fluoric acid
acid of sparry .... fluoric acid
acid of sugar .... oxalic acid
acid of sugar of milk .... mucous acid
acid of tungsten .... tungstic acid
acid of vitriol .... sulphuric acid
acid of vitriol, phlogisticated .... sulphurous acid
acid of wolfram .... tungstic acid
acid of wood sorrel .... oxalic acid
acid spirit of phosphorus .... phosphoric acid
acid, dephlogisticated marine .... oxygenized muriatic acid
acids, mineral .... sulphuric, hydrochloric & nitric
acidulous .... sour
acidum aceticum dilutum .... acetic acid diluted
acidum arsenosum .... white arsenic
acidum benzoicum .... benzoic acid
acidum boricum .... boric acid
acidum carbolicum .... carbolic acid
acidum citricum .... citric acid
acidum hydrocyanicum dilutum .... prussic acid
acidum hypophosphorous dilutum .... diluted hydrophorus acid
acidum lacticum .... lactic acid
acidum nitricum dilutum .... diluted nitric acid
acidum oleicum .... oleic acid
acidum phosphoricum .... phosphoric acid
acidum salicylicum .... salicylic acid
acidum stearicum .... stearic acid from solid fats
acidum sulphurosum .... sulphuric acid
acidum tannicum .... tannic acid, from nutgall
acidum tartaricum .... tartaric acid
aconitum .... aconite phosphoric acid
adamantine sapr .... aluminum oxide
adamas .... diamond, lodestone
adeps lanae .... lanolin, wool fat
adipic acid .... adipinic acid, hexandioic acid
aerated soda water .... water charged with carbonic acid gas
aerial chalk acid .... carbon dioxide
air .... any colorless gas
air, alkaline .... ammoniacal gas
air, dephlogisticated .... oxygen

air, dephlogisticated marine acid .... oxygenized muriatic acid gas
air, empyreal .... oxygen
air, fetid of sulphur .... sulphuretted hydrogen gas
air, fixed .... carbonic acid gas
air, heptic .... sulphuretted hydrogen gas
air, impure or vitiated .... nitrogen, azote, azotic gas
air, inflammable .... hydrogen gas
air, marine acid .... muriatic acid gas
air, phlogisticated .... nitrogen, azote, azotic gas
air, pure .... oxygen
air, solid, of Hales .... carbonic acid gas
air, vital .... oxygen
al kohl .... antimony sulphide
alabandite .... manganese sulphide
alabaster .... gypsum
alapurin .... adeps lanae
alcohol .... (originally) powdered antimony;
.... (later)any condensed sublimate or distillate
alcohol dilutum .... diluted alcohol spirit
alcohol of sulphur .... flowers of sulphur
alcohol of wine .... distilled ethyl alcohol
alcohol, amyl, normal .... fusel oil, grain oil & pentanol
alcohol, methyl .... wood alcohol
alcohol, pure .... grain alcohol, cologne spirits
aldehyde.. acetaldehyde
algaroth, powder of ... white oxide of antimony by the muriatic acid
algic acid .... algin acid
alizarin .... dye produced artificially from anthracine
alkali .... potash
alkali, concrete volatile .... carbonate of ammonia
alkali, marine .... soda
alkali, mineral .... soda
alkali, prussian .... prussiate of potass
alkali, vegetable .... potash
alkali, volatile .... ammonia
alkalies............................... caustic substances such as soda ash
alkalies, caustic ... pure alkalies, or those deprived of carbonic acid
alkalies, effervescent...................................... alkaline carbonates,
.... or alkalies combined with carbonic acid
alkalies, fixed .... potash and soda
alkaline air .... ammonia
alkaline antimoniate .... term for any salt of antimonic acid
allium .... garlic
allom.. alum
alloxan .... formed by the action of nitric acid on uric acid
aloe barbadensis .... aloe vera
aloe socotrina .... aloe perryi
althaea paper .... test paper from hollyhock flowers
alum .... potash alum, potassium aluminum sulphate,
.... sulphate of alumine and potass

alum meal .... potash alum
alumen .... dried or burnt alum
alumina .... aluminum oxide
alumini hydras .... aluminum hydrate
alumini sulphas .... aluminum sulphate
aluminum .... silvery white metal
aluminum acetate .... mordant salt, red liquor
aluminum chloride .... sesquichloride of aluminum
aluminum hydrate .... aluminum hydroxide
aluminum hydroxide .... aluminum hydrate, diaspore
aluminum oxide .... alumina
aluminum sulphate .... cake alum, papermakers alum
alundum .... fused aluminum oxide
alunogen .... aluminum sulphate
amber seed .... musk seed
amboyna .... clove oil
ambrosia .... essence of wormwood
american asheds .... potassium carbonate
american pearlash .... locally refined potassium carbonate
amianthus .... asbestos
aminiphen .... aniline
aminoform .... hexamethylenetetramine
amminii bromidum .... ammonium bromide
ammonia alum .... aluminum ammonium sulphate
ammonia chrome alum .... chromium ammonium sulphate
ammonia crystals .... ammonium carbonate
ammonia soap .... ammonium oleate
ammonia water .... aqua ammonia
ammonia, anhydrous .... liquid ammonia
ammonia, aqua .... ammonium hydroxide
ammoniac chloride muriate of ammonia .... ammonium chloride
ammoniacal sulphate of copper .... ammonio-sulphate of copper
ammoniacum .... ammoniac
ammoniated copper .... solution of cupric ions in ammonia
ammonical secret salt of glauber .... ammonium sulphate
ammonii benzoas .... ammonium benzoate
ammonii carbonas .... ammonium carbonate
ammonii chloridum .... ammonium chloride
ammonii iodidum .... ammonium iodide
ammonio-chloride of mercury .... mercuric ammonium chloride
ammonio-citrate of iron .... ammonio-ferric acid citrate
ammonio-ferric alum .... ammonio-ferric citrate
ammonio-ferric citrate .... ammonio-citrate of iron
ammonio-ferric sulphate .... sulphate of iron & ammonium
ammonio-hydric carbonate .... ammonium bicarbonate
ammonium acetate .... spirit of minderus
ammonium bifluoride .... hydrogen ammonium fluoride
ammonium carbonate .... ammonia crystals
ammonium chloride .... sal ammoniac & ammonium muriate
ammonium hydroxide .... aqua ammonia

7

ammonium iodide................hydroiodate of ammonia
ammonium muriate.......................ammonium chloride
ammonium phosphate.............. di-ammonium phosphate
ammonium sesquicarbonate.......................... smelling salt
ammonium sulphocyanate................. ammonium sulphocyanide
ammonium sulphocyanide................. ammonium sulphocyanate
ammoniuret of gold............................. fulminate of gold
amyl acetate................................ banana oil; pearl oil
amyl valeriate.. apple oil
amylum.. starch
anglesite.................................... lead sulphate
anhydrous alcohol................................ absolute alcohol
anhydrous protoxide of tin..................... stannous oxide
animal black .... bone charcoal
animal charcoal.. bone black
antichlor.................................... sodium thiosulphate
antimoniate of potash.......................... calcined antimony
antimonii et potassi tartras .... tartar emetic
antimonii sulphidum..................................... antimony sulphide
antimonious chloride....................... antimony chloride
antimonious oxide............................. antimony trioxide
antimonyantimony sulphide, any condensed sublimate or distillate
antimony bloom .... antimony trioxide
antimony glace.................................. antimony sulphide – black
antimony, crude .... sulphuret of antimony
antimony, diaphoretic.......... white oxide of antimony by nitric acid
aperient.. laxative
apocynum .... canadian hemp
apple oil .... amyl valerianate
aqua ammoniæ .... ammonia water
aqua ammonia .... ammonium hydroxide
aqua ammonia pura .... ammonia
aqua anisi .... anise water
aqua ardens .... dilute solution of alcohol in water
aqua camphoræ .... camphor water
aqua destillata.. distilled water
aqua foeeniculi .... fennel water
aqua fortis .... nitric acid
aqua hydrogeniidioxidi .... hydrogen dioxide
aqua regia .... nitric & hydrochloric acids
aqua valens .... nitric, hydrochloric, or sulphuric acid
aqua vitae .... strong solution of alcohol in water
archil .... orchil, a purple dye from lichens
ardent spirits.. strong liquor
argentan.. nickel-silver
argenti cyanidum .... silver cyanide
argenti iodidum .... silver iodide
argenti nitras .... silver nitrate
argenti nitras fusus .... lunar castic
argenti oxidum ....silver oxide

8

argentite .... silver sulphide
argentum ....silver
argil, argillaceious earth .... aluminae
argols .... crude cream of tartar
arnicæ flores .... arnica flower
aromatic spirits of ammonia .... ammonium hydroxide
arsenamine .... arsenic hydride
arsenate of potash ....potassium arsenate
arseneted hydrogen .... arsenic hydride
arseni iodidum .... arsenic iodide
arsenic hydride .... arsenamine
arsenolite ....arsenic
asbestos .... magnesium silicate
asbolite .... cobalt oxide
asclepias .... pleurisy root
asfoetida .... asafetida
ash of lead ....artificial lead sulphide
ash of musk ivy .... potash
asphaltum .... asphalt, mineral pitch
aspidium .... male fern
atropinæ .... atropine, deadly nightshade
auri et sodii cloridum .... gold & sodium chloride
aurichalcum, orichalcum........................... brass, bronze
auripigmentum .... yellow arsenic suiphide
aurous chloride .... gold chloride
aurous oxide .... gold oxide
aurum .... gold
azote .... nitrogen
azotic acid .... nitric acid
azure .... basic copper carbonate,
.... copper carbonate plus copper silicate
bahnmetal .... lead-lithium alloy
baking soda .... sodium bicarbonate
balm of mecca .... balm of gilead
balsam .... canada balsam
balsam of copaiba.. copaiba
banana oil .... amyl acetate
barilla .... carbonate of soda
barite .... barium sulphate
barium monosulphide .... barium sulphide
barium sulphide ....barium monosulphide
baryta ....barium oxide
baryta, heavy spar ....barium oxide
barytes .... barium sulphate
base of air .... oxygen
basic lead citrate .... tribasic lead acetate
basic mercuric sulphate .... mercurous sulphate
basic nitrate of bismuth .... bismuth subnitrate
bauxite .... impure aluminum oxide
bell-metal .... a copper-tin bronze

belladonnæ folia .... belladonna leaves
belladonnæ radix .... belladonna root
benjamin .... benzoic acid
benzene .... benzol
benzine .... gasoline, petroleum
benzinum .... benzine
benzoar mineral .... oxide of antimony
benzoic ether .... ethyl benzoate
benzoinum .... balsamic resin, benzoin
betula oil .... oil of wintergreen
bicarbonate of ammonia .... ammonium bicarbonate
bicarbonate of potassa .... potassium bicarbonate
bicarbonate of soda .... sodium bicarbonate
bicarburet of hydrogen .... ethylene
bichloride of copper .... cuprous chloride
bichloride of mercury .... mercuric chloride
bichloride of platinum .... platinous chloride
bichloride of tin .... stannous chloride
bichromate of ammonia .... ammonium bichromate
bichromate of potash .... potassium dichromate
bicyanide of mercury .... mercuric cyanide
binoxide of tin .... stannic oxide
bisemutum .... bismuth
bismuthi et ammonii citras .... bismuth & ammonia citrate
bismuthous oxide .... bismuth trioxide
bisulphate of potash .... potassium bisulphate
bisulphate of soda .... sodium bisulphate
bisulphide of carbon .... carbon disulphide
bisulphide of mercury .... mercuric sulphide
bisulphite of potash .... potassium hydrogen sulphite
bisulphuret of carbon .... carbon disulphide
bisulphuret of iron .... pyrite (ferric bisulphide)
bisulphuret of tin .... stannic sulphide
bitartrate of potassa .... potassium bitartrate
bitter apple .... colocynth
bitumin .... jet, obsidian, camphor, amber, pitch, tar, coal
black antimony sulphide .... antimony sulphide
black bismuth .... bismuth sulphide
black boy gum .... accroides gum
black cohosh .... black snake root
black copper .... copper oxide
black jack .... zinc sulphide
black lead .... graphite, hyper-carburet of iron
black liquor .... protoacetate of iron
black magnesium .... manganese dioxide
black oxide of cobalt .... cobalt oxide
black oxide of copper .... cupric oxide
black oxide of manganese .... manganous peroxide
black oxide of mercury .... mercurous oxide
black pitch .... asphalt

10

black precipitate .... mercurous oxide
black resin .... common resin – dark
black sulphur .... sulphur vivum
blanc fixe .... barium sulphate, artifical
bleaching powder .... calcium hypochlorite, chloride of lime
blende .... calamine (zinc sulphide)
bleu d'azure .... smalt
blood, red .... red iron oxide
blubber oil .... whale oil
blue copperas .... copper sulphate, cupric sulphate
blue galls .... aleppo galls
blue malachite,artifical .... copper carbonate, blue
blue salt .... nickel sulphate
blue stone .... copper sulphate
blue verditer .... azurite blue
blue vitriol .... copper sulphate, cupric sulphate
body oil .... whale oil
boiled oil .... boiled linseed oil
bole armoniac powder .... Armenian clay
bolognian phosphorus .... barium sulphate
bolus alba .... china clay
bone ash .... calcium phosphate
bone black .... animal charcoal
bone dust .... bone meal
bone oil .... dippel and hartshorn oil
boneset .... comfrey
boracic acid .... boric acid
boras .... borax
borate of soda .... sodium borate
borax .... sodium borate, sodium tetraborate
bordeau mixture .... copper sulfate, quick lime and water
borneol .... borneo camphor
brass .... copper
brazil wax .... carnauba wax
bremen blue .... copper carbonate, blue
bremen green .... copper carbonate
brimstone .... sulphur
britannia metal .... alloy of tin, copper and antimony
british gum .... dextrin
bromate of potash .... potassium bromate
bromo "acid" .... tetrabrom fluorescein
brown red .... ferric oxide
brown spar .... dolomite
brucite .... magnesium hydroxide
bublum oil .... neatsfoot oil
bugbane .... cimifuga
burning water .... solution of alcohol in water
burnt alum .... dehydrated alum
burnt borax .... calcined sodium borate
burnt ivory .... bones burned to a powder

11

burnt ocher .... red iron oxide
burnt sugar .... caramel
burnt tartar .... potassium carbonate
butanol .... butyl alcohol
butter color .... annatto
butter of antimony .... antimony chloride,
.... antimony trichloride, muriate of antimony
butter of caliche .... impure sodium nitrate and chloride
butter of tin .... stannic chloride
butter of zinc .... zinc chloride
buttercup yellow .... zinc chromate
butyl carbitol .... diethylene glycol monobutyl ether
butyrone .... dipropyl ketone
byronia .... bryony
cachou .... cutch
cadmia .... kobelt, ore of cadmium sulphide and carbonate
cadmium iodide ....hydroiodate of cadmium
cadmium sulphide .... jaune brillant, greenockite
cadmium tungstate .... cadmium wolframate
cadmium yellow .... cadmium sulphide
caffeina citrata .... citrated caffeine
cake alum .... aluminum sulphate
calamine ....zinc silicate, zinc sulphide
calamus ....sweet flag
calc .... oxide
calc spar .... calcium carbonate
calces, metallic .... metallic oxides
calcic carbonate .... calcium carbonate
calcic hydrate ....calcium hydroxide
calcic liver of sulphur .... calcium sulphide & lime sulphur
calcii bromidum .... calcium bromide
calcii chloridium........................ calcium chloride; lime & chloride
calcii hypophosphis .... calcium hypophosphite
calcii sulphas exsiccatus .... dried gypsum
calcimine.. kalsomine
calcinated alum .... alum burned to a powder
calcined antimony .... diaphoretic antimony
calcined baryta ....barium oxide
calcined magnesia .... magnesium oxide
calcined oyster shells...calcium oxide
calcined plaster .... calcium sulphate
calcined soda .... sodium oxide
calcined sulphate of iron .... calcined ferric sulphate
calcite .... calcium carbonate
calcium carbide .... acetylenogen
calcium carbonate .... whiting, precipitated chalk
calcium cyanamide .... cyanamide
calcium fluoride .... fluorspar
calcium monosulphide .... calcium sulphide
calcium monoxide .... calcium oxide

calcium nitrate ....lime saltpeter, nitrate of lime
calcium oxide .... lime, quicklime
calcium phosphate .... bone ash
calcium phosphate, acid .... calcium phosphate, monobasic
calcium sulphide .... calcic liver of sulphur
calcium tungstate .... normal calcium wolframate
calendula .... marigold
caliche .... sodium nitrate
calomel .... mercurous chloride
caloric .... heat
calx .... lime
calx chlorinata .... bleaching powder, chlorinated lime
calx sulphurata .... lime sulphur, sulphurated lime
cambogia .... gum gamboge
camfire .... henna
camphire .... camphor
camphor .... gum champhor
camwood .... barwood
canada balsam .... fir balsam, yellow liquid
canadol .... benzine & petroleum ether
canarium .... gum elemi
cannabis indica .... indian hemp
cantharis .... spanish flies
caouchouc .... india rubber, latex, elastic gum
capsicum.. cayenne pepper, red pepper
caput mortuum .... red iron oxide
carbamide .... urea
carbazole .... diphenylimide
carbo animalis.................................... animal charcoal
carbo ligni .... charcoal
carbolic acid .... phenol
carbon bichloride .... tetrachlorethylene
carbon bisulphide.............................. carbon disulphide
carbon dichloride .... tetrachlorethylene
carbon dioxide .... carbonic acid
carbon monoxide .... carbonic oxide
carbon sulphide .... carbon disulphide
carbon tetrachloride .... benzinoform
carbonate of potassa .... cream of tartar
carbone .... charcoal
carbonic acid gas................................... carbon dioxide
carbonic anhydride............................... carbon dioxide
carbonic gas .... carbon dioxide
carbonicum .... carbon
carborundum .... silicon carbide
carboxy-propylene .... crotonic acid
carbro tissue .... photographic material
carburet of iron .... graphite
carburet of sulphur .... carbon disulphide
carmine .... red color make from cochineal

13

carnauba wax .... brazil wax
carnots reagent .... bismuth nitrate
carragheen .... irish moss
caryophil oil .... clove oil
cashoo .... cutch
cassel brown .... vandyke brown
cassiterite .... stannic oxide
castile soap .... olive oil soap
castor bean .... riciumus & mexico seed
castor meal .... castor pomace
catechol .... pyrocatechol
catechu .... a dying and tanning substance
cathartic .... strong laxative
caustic antimony .... antimony chloride
caustic baryta .... barium hydroxide, barium oxide
caustic of potassa .... hydrate of potassium
caustic potash .... potassium hydroxide
caustic soda .... sodium hydroxide, lye
caustic, lunar .... fused nitrate of silver
cch .... hypochlorite in dry form
cedrate .... citron
cellulose acetate .... acetyl cellulose
cenobrium .... vermilion
ceresin wax .... cerosin wax, mineral wax
ceruleo sulphate of ammonia .... ammonium sulphate
ceruleo sulphate of potassa .... potassium sulphate
ceruse .... white oxide of lead by the acetous acid
ceruse of antimony .... white oxide of antimony by precipitation
cerussite .... lead carbonate
cetaceum .... spermaceti
cetraria .... iceland moss
cetylic acid .... palmitic acid
cevadilla .... sabadilla
ceylon cinnamon .... ceylones cinnamomum zeylanicum
ceyssatite .... diatomaceous earth
chalcanthum .... iron sulphate
chalcedony .... quartz
chalcitis .... cupriferous pyrites
chalcontrite .... cupric sulphate
chalk .... calcium carbonate, carbonate of lime
chamber lye .... urine
chamomile .... camomile
charcoal, pine .... carbon
charta potassil-nitratis .... potassium nitrate paper
charta sinapis .... mustard paper
checkerberry .... oil of wintergreen
chemical red .... red iron oxide
chenopodium .... american wormseed
chicle gum .... gum chicle
chicle substitute .... gum aroban

14

child of Saturn .... antimony
chile saltpetre .... sodium nitrate
chili saltpeter .... sodium nitrate
china bark .... soap bark
china clay .... kaolin
china wood oil .... tung oil
chinchona .... cinchona
chinese bean oil .... soya bean oil
chinese wax .... insect wax
chinese white .... zinc oxide pigment
chip soap .... soap flakes
chloral .... chloral hydrate
chloralum .... aluminum chloride
chlorethane .... ethyl chloride
chloric gas .... chlorine
chloride of gormile .... chloroform
chloride of lime .... bleaching powder, calcium hypochlorite
chlorine water .... common bleach
chloroform .... trichloromethane, formyl trichloride
chloromethane .... methyl chloride
choke damp .... carbonic acid gas
cholestrin .... cholesterol
chondrus .... irish moss
chrome alum .... chromium potassium sulphate
chrome green .... chromium oxide, chromous oxide
chrome iron stone .... chromite
chrome orange .... lead dichromate
chrome ore .... chromite
chrome yellow .... lead chromate
chromic acid.................................... chromium trioxide
chromium phosphate .... arnaudon's green
chromium sulphate .... wool mordant
cinnabar...... mercuric sulphide, red sulphuretted oxide of mercury
citric acid .... oxytricarballylic acid
citron yellow .... zinc chromate
citronella oil .... verbena oil
claret...red wine
clove oil .... carophil oil, amboyna
coal tar creosote .... phenol
coaly .... containing carbon
cobalt black.. cobalt oxide
cobalt blue ....azure blue
cobalt linoleate .... cobaltous linoleate
cobalt sesquioxide .... cobalt peroxide
cobalt yellow.......................... cobalt potassium nitrite
cocainæ hydrochloras............... hydrochlorate of cocaine
cochineal .... coccus
coconut cake .... copra cake
cod liver oil .... banks oil & morrhua oil
codeina .... alkaloid from opium

15

codoil .... rosin oil
cognac oil .... oenanthic ether
colcothar .... ferric oxide
collodion .... nitrocellulose, pyroxylin
collodium .... pyroxylin, ether & alcohol
colloidal clay .... bentonite
cologne spirits .... alcohol
colonial spirits .... methanol
colophony .... rosin; pine resin
colothar .... red iron oxide
colthothar of vitrol .... red oxide of iron, by the sulphuric acid
columbian spirits .... methanol
columbium .... niobium
colza .... rapeseed
colza oil .... rapeseed oil
compound ethers... ester
concentrated alum .... aluminum sulphate
conine, coniine .... hemlock
conterfei ....zinc
coomb .... four bushels
copper acetate .... green verdigris
copper aceto arsentite ....paris green
copper arsenite........ mineral green, swedish green, scheele's green
copper carbonate .... artificial malachite
copper cyanide .... cupric cyanide
copper flowers .... cupric oxide
copper glance .... copper sulphide
copper nitrate .... cupric nitrate
copper oxide .... cupric oxide
copper pyrite .... copper iron sulphide
copper scale .... artificial copper oxide
copper subacetate .... basic copper acetate & green verdigris
copper sulphate............... blue vitriol, blue stone, cupric sulphate
copper vitriol .... copper sulphate
copper, acetated .... acetate of copper
copperas .... ferrous sulphate
copperas blue .... sulphate of copper
copperas, green .... sulphate of iron
copperas, green vitriol .... ferrous sulphate
copra.. dried coconut meat
corcus martis ....ferric hydroxide
corn oil....................................... maize oil, pale yellow liquid
corn starch... maranta & amylam
corn sugar .... glucose, dextrose
corn syrup... glucose
cornish clay .... china clay
corrosive chloride of mercury .... mercuric chloride
corrosive sublimate .... mercuric chloride
corundum .... aluminum oxide
cosmetic bismuth .... bismuth oxychloride

16

cosmetic mercury .... mercuric ammonuim chloride
cosmoline .... petrolatum
coumarin .... cumarin, tonka bean camphor
coumarone resin .... paracoumarone
crawly root .... coral root, corallorhiza odontorhiza
cream of tartar .... potassium bitartrate, supertartrate of potass
creosotum .... mixture of phenols of wood-tar
cresol .... creasylic acid
creta præparata .... prepared chalk
creta praecipitata .... calcium carbonate
crocus .... ferric oxide, saffron
crocus of antimony .... antimony sulphide
crocus powder .... ferric oxide
crude antimony .... antimony sulphide
crude native sulphur .... sulphur
crude oil .... petroleum
crude tartar .... unprocessed potassium bitartrate
crystallized soda .... crystalline sodium carbonate
crystallized verdigris .... copper acetate
crystals of tartar .... potassium bitartrate
crystals of tin .... stannous chloride
crystals of venus .... copper acetate
cuba wood .... fustic
cube alum .... potash alum
cubic nitre .... sodium nitrate
cudbear .... orchil, archil
culcifuge .... mosquito and flea repeliant
cullender .... collander
cupri sulphas .... copper sulphate
cupric chloride .... chloride of copper
cupric ferrocyanide .... prussiate of copper
cupric oxide .... tenorite
cupric sulphate .... blue stone; blue vitriol
cuprite .... cuprous oxide
cuprum .... copper
curcuma .... turmeric
curry .... turmeric
cutch .... gum catechu, cashao
cyanamid .... calcium cyanamide
cyanate of ammonia .... heated urea
cyanate of potassa .... potassium cyanate
cyanate of silver .... silver cyanate
cyanide of mercury .... mercuric cyanide
cyanuret .... cyanide
cyanuret of potassium .... potassium cyanide
cyanuret of zinc .... zinc cyanide
cymene .... isopropyltoluene, paracymol
cyprium .... copper
cystogen .... hexamethylenetetramine
dead oil .... creosote oil

17

decalin .... decahydronaphthalene
decolorizing carbons .... bone black
degras .... wool grease
deutoxide of barium .... barium peroxide
deutoxide of copper .... cupric oxide
deutoxide of hydrogen .... hydrogen peroxide
deutoxide of manganese .... manganese dioxide
deutoxide of mercury .... mercuric oxide
dextrin .... british gum, starch gum
di-ammonic carbonate .... ammonium carbonate
diacetate of lead .... tribasic lead acetate
diamantine .... corundum
diaphoretic .... sudorific
diaphoretic antimony .... calcined antimony
diaspore .... aluminum hydroxide
diastase .... diastafor, diastasum
diatomaceous earth .... infusorial earth, kieselguhr, fossil flour
dibasic carbonate of copper .... copper carbonate
dichloride of manganese .... manganese chloride
dichloride of platinum .... platinous chloride
dichloride of tin .... stannous chloride
dichromate of lead .... lead dichromate
digallic acid ....tannic acid
digestive salt of silvius .... potassium acetate
dihydric sulphide .... hydrogen sulphide
dioxide of copper .... cupric oxide
dioxide of mercury .... mercurous oxide
dioxide of tin .... stannic oxide
diphenylimide .... carbazole& iminodiphenyl
dipotassic carbonate .... potassium carbonate
dipotassic sulphate .... potassium sulphate
dippel ....bone oil
dipping acid ....sulphuric acid
dipropyl ketone .... butyrone
disodic orthophosphate .... sodium phosphate
disulphate of quinia............................... quinine sulphate
disulphide ....bisulphide
diuretic salt .... potassium acetate
dolomite .... brown spar
dolomol ....magnesium stearate
dope .... pyroxylin solution
dowmetal...................................... magnesium alloys
dragon gum .... gum tragacanth
dreft .... wetting agent
dried lees of vinegar.............................. cream of tartar
dried lees of wine.................................... cream of tartar
drop black .... frankfort black
dry acetic acid .... anhydrous acetic acid
dry ice .... solid carbon dioxide
duresco .... lithopone

dutch liquid .... ethylene chloride, ethylene dichloride
dutch metal .... a variety of brass
dyer's acetate of iron .... protoacetate of iron
earth of alum .... alumine
earth of siliceous .... silex
earth wax .... ceresin wax
earth, aluminous .... alumine
earth, calcareous .... lime
earth, infusorial .... earth, diatomaceous
earth, magnesian .... magnesia
earth, muriatic .... magnesia
earth, ponderous .... barytes
earthnut oil .... peanut oil
east indian copaiba .... balsam gurjun
eau de javelle .... sodium hypochlorite
ebonite .... black hard rubber
egg oil .... egg yolk
egg, white of .... albumen
eka-aluminum .... gallium
eka-silicon .... germanium
elaic acid .... oleic acid
elaidic acid .... oleic acid
elastic gum .... rubber, latex
elaterite .... mineral rubber
electica .... india rubber
electrum .... amber, natural alloy of gold & silver
emerald .... beryl
emerald green .... copper acetoarsenite
emeraude green .... guignet green
emerick .... emery
emery .... aluminum oxide, aluminum oxide fused with magnetite
emetic tartar .... antimoniated tartrate of potass, antimony tartrate
emplastrum .... plaster
enamel white .... lithopone
english red .... red iron oxide
english white .... calcium carbonate
epsom salts .... magnesium sulphate
erytronium .... vanadium
escharotic... caustic
essence of mirbane .... nitrobenzene
essence of niobe .... methyl benzoate
essences .... volatile oil
essential oil of lemons .... potassium binoxalate
ethal .... cetyl alcohol
ethalic acid .... palmitic acid
ethanal .... acetaldehyde
ethanamide .... acetamide
ethandioic acid .... oxalic acid
ethanol .... ethyl alcohol
ether .... ethyl ether, ethyl oxide

ethiops per se .... black sulphuretted oxide of mercury
ethiops, martial ....black oxide of iron
ethiops, mineral .... black sulphuretted oxide of mercury
ethyl aldehyde .... acetaldehyde
ethyl benzene .... phenylethane; xylene
ethyl butyrate .... pinapple oil
ethyl chloride .... muriatic ether
ethyl iodide.................................... iodethane hydriotic ether
ethyl nitrite .... nitrous ether,fir
ethylene ....ethene, etherin, elayl
ethylene dichloride ....ethylene chloride
ethylene tetrachloride .... acetylene tetrachloride
ethylic ether .... ethyl oxide
eunatrol .... sodium oleate
eupatorium .... thoroughwort
extract of lead..lead diacetate
extract of saturn..lead diacetate
faience .... a greenish blue quartz glass
feather alum... aluminum sulphate
febrifuge salt .... potassium chloride
febrifuge salt of silvius .... potassium chloride
fecula .... starch
feints .... faints
fel bovis .... ox bile
felxoresins .... synthetic resins
ferri carbonas saccharatus .... sugared iron carbonate
ferri chloridum .... iron chloride
ferri citras .... iron citrate
ferri et ammoii tartaras............................ iron & ammoniatartrate
ferri et ammonii citras .... iron & ammonia citrate
ferri et ammonii sulphas........................ iron & ammonia sulphate
ferri sulphas .... iron sulphate
ferric chloride .... iron chloride
ferric ferrocyanide .... berlin blue ferrocyanide of iron
ferric hydroxide .... iron hydroxide
ferric nitrate ....protonitrate of iron
ferric orthophosphate .... ferric phosphate
ferric oxide .... brown red; colcothar; crocus
ferrochyazic acid .... hydroferrocyanic acid
ferrocyanic acid .... paris blue
ferrous acetate .... acetate of iron
ferrous ammonium sulphate .... copperas, iron vitriol
ferrous carbonate .... subcarbonate of iron
ferrous chloride .... muriate of iron
ferrous oxide .... monoxide of iron
ferrous sulphate .... copperas; green vitriol
ferrous sulphide .... iron sulphide, iron sulphuret
ferrum..iron
festoform .... formaldehyde
fire air .... oxygen

20

fire damp ...... methane
fischers yellow ...... cobalt potassium nitrite
fish glue ...... isinglass
fixed alkali salts ...... carbonates
fixed ammoniacal salt ...... calcium chloride
fixed nitre ...... potassium carbonate
flake white ...... bismuth subnitrate, lead carbonate
flaxseed ...... linseed
flea-seed ...... psyllium
fleabane ...... pennyroyal
fleaseed ...... psyllium seed
florence oil ...... olive oil
flores martis ...... ferric chloride
florspar ...... calcium fluoride
flowers of antimony ...... antimony oxide
flowers of bismuth ...... bismuth trioxide
flowers of sulphur ..... sublimated metallic oxides sulphur, sulphur
flowers of tin ...... tin oxide
flowers of tin stone ...... tin peroxide
flowers of zinc ...... zinc oxide
flowers, metallic ...... sublimated metallic oxides
fluid silver ...... mercury
fluores ...... fluorite, calcium fluoride
fluoric acid ...... hydrofluoric acid
fluorol ...... sodium fluoride
fluors ...... fluates
fluorspar ...... calcium fluoride
flutonium ...... barium
fools gold ...... iron pyrites
formaldehyde ...... methyl aldehyde
formalin ...... formaldehyde (40% solution)
formic acid ...... methanoic acid
formin ...... hexamethylenetetramine
formosa camphor ...... camphor
fossil wax ...... ozokerite wax
foul air ...... nitrogen
frankincense ...... gum thus
french chalk ...... talc
fructose ...... levulose
fuccus crispus ...... irish moss
fuchin ...... magenta
fuchsine ...... magenta
fuming liquor of arsenic ...... arsenic trichloride
fuming liquor of Labavius ...... stannous chloride
fuming spirit of niter ...... fuming nitric acid
fuming sulphuric acid ...... pyrosulphuric acid
fused nitrate of strontia ...... melted strontium nitrate
fusel oil ...... amyl alcohol, potato oil
fustic ...... wood fustic & cubic wood

galena .... lead sulphide, lead sulphit,
.... litharge, natural lead sulphide
gallate of iron .... ferrous gallate
gallic acid .... trihydroxybenzoic acid
galline .... pyrogallic acid
gallotanic acid .... tannic acid
galls .... nutgalls
gambier extract .... pale catechu & terra saponica
gamboge .... gum resin
garancine .... madder-red
gas sylvestre .... carbon dioxide
gaseous oxide of carbon .... carbonic oxide
gaultheria oil .... oil of wintergreen
gelatin .... glutin
gelbin .... barium chromate
gem salt .... rock salt crystals
german soda .... sodium hydroxide strength of 95%
germantown black .... carbon black
gesso .... mixture of whiting and an adhesive
gigely oil .... sesame oil
gilder's white .... whiting
glaire .... egg white
glance pitch .... manjak
glantz .... galena (lead sulphide)
glass liquor...................................... sodium silicate
glass of bismuth .... vitreous oxide of bismuth
glass of borax .... calcined borax
glass soap .... natural manganese dioxide
glass, water .... sodium silicate
glauber's salt .... sodium sulphate
glauber's secret salt...................................... ammonium sulphate
glauberite .... sodium sulphate
glucinium .... beryllium
glucose .... corn sugar, grape sugar
glue or jelly.. gelatine
glutinous matter.. gluten
glycerin .... glycerol
glycerinum .... glycerin, from decomposion of fats
glycol... ethylene glycol
glycol dichloride .... ethlene chloride
glycol oleate.. diglycol oleate
glyptal .... synthetic resin
gold chloride .... soluble gold salt
gold monochloride .... aurous chloride
gold purple .... purple of cassius
golden sulphuret of antimony .... antimony pentasulphide
gommeline.. dextrin
goslarite .... zinc sulphate
goulard's extract.................................... tribasic lead acetate
goulard's lotion.................................... tribasic lead acetate

goulard's water .... lead acetate solution
goulards powder .... lead acetate
grain alcohol .... ethyl alcohol, ethanol
grain oil .... alcohol, amyl
graphite .... plumbago, black lead
gray antimony .... antimony sulphide
gray bismuth .... bismuth sulphide
gray oxide of antimony .... antimony glass
gray oxide of cobalt .... cobalt oxide
green chrysocolla .... malachite
green cinnabar .... chromium oxide
green copperas .... ferrous sulphate
green nickel oxide .... nickel oxide
green oil .... chromium oxide
green soap .... soft soap
green verdigris .... copper acetate
green vitriol .... ferrous sulphate
greencopper carbonate .... copper carbonate
greenland spar .... cryolite
greenockite .... cadmium sulphide
griffith's white .... lithopone
ground nut oil .... peanut oil
guaiac resin .... gum guaiac
guano .... dry excrement of sea birds
guhr .... diatomaceous earth
guinet's green .... viridian, permanent green
gum accroides .... black boy gum
gum ammoniac .... ammoniac
gum arabic .... acacia gum, senegal gum
gum aroban .... chicle substitute
gum benzoin .... gum benjamin, benzoin resin
gum chicle .... balata, zapota gum
gum congo .... copal resin
gum copal .... anime, kauri
gum dammar .... damar resin
gum elemi .... canarium and manila elemi
gum gambier .... terra japonica & pale catechu
gum lac .... shellac
gum mastic .... mastiche & pistachia galls
gum pontianak .... jelutong
gum rosin .... colophony, yellow resin
gum sandarac .... juniper gum
gum thus .... frankincense & olibanum
gumtree .... gum accroides
guncotton .... nitrocellulose
gunderfai .... electrum
gutta-percha .... sumatera gum, relative of rubber
gypsum .... calcium sulphate, sulphate of lime
haematoxylum .... logwood
hair salt .... aluminum sulphate

23

halite .... sodium chloride
hamamelis .... witch hazel
hard lead .... antimonial lead
hartshorn .... ammonia in H2O solution
hartshorn oil .... bone oil
hearth lead .... litharge
heavy spar .... barium sulphate
hedeoma .... pennyroyal
hellebore root .... veratrum viride
hematite .... iron oxide
hematitic .... red iron ore
hepar of sulphur .... potassium sulphide
hepars .... sulphurets
hermus mineral .... red sulphuretted oxide of antimony
hexadecylic acid .... palmitic acid
hexamethylenetetramine .... urotropin, aminoform
hexamine .... hexamethylenetetramine
hog gum .... gum tragacanth
hoofoil .... neatsfoot oil
horn quicksilver .... mercuric chloride
horn silver .... silver chloride
hth .... calcium hypochlorite in dry form
huiles .... french for oils
humulus .... hops
hungarian antimony .... stibnite (antimony trisulphide)
hurr nuts .... myrobalan extract
hyacinth .... zircon silicate
hydrargium .... mercury
hydrated benzoyl .... benzoic acid
hydrated sulphuric ether .... ethyl oxide
hydride of phenyl .... benzine
hydriodate of iron .... ferric iodide
hydrobromic acid .... hydrogen bromide
hydrochlorate of ammonia .... ammonium chloride
hydrochloric acid .... muriatic acid
hydrofluoric acid .... fluohydric acid & hydrogen fluoride
hydrogen peroxide .... perhydrol
hydrogen sulphide .... sulphuretted hydrogen
hydroiodate of cadmium .... cadmium iodide
hydroresin .... synthetic resin
hydrosodic carbonate .... sodium bicarbonate
hydrosodic phosphate .... sodium phosphate
hydrosulphite .... sodium hydrosulphite
hydroxl .... hydrogen peroxide
hypo .... sodium thiosulphate
hypochlorite of lime .... bleaching powder, calcium hypochlorite
ice stone .... cryolite
iceland spar .... calcite, calcium carbonate
ichthyocolla .... isinglass
ichthyol .... ammonium sulfo ichthyolate

24

idene .... paracoumarone
imperial green .... copper acetoarsenite
indene .... para-cumarone
india red .... ferric oxide
indian gum .... gum karaya
indian red .... red iron oxide
indian rubber .... latex, rubber
indian saffron .... turmeric
infusorial earth .... diatomaceous earth
insect powder .... pyrethrum
insect wax .... chinese wax
iodate of soda .... sodium iodate
iodum .... a heavy metal
iohydric acid .... hydrogen iodide
ipecac root .... ipecacuanha & uraquoga
irish moss .... carragheen, chondrush
iron carbide .... graphite
iron ethiops .... iron oxide
iron oxide .... ferric oxide
iron peroxide .... ferric oxide
iron pyrites .... iron disulphide
iron vitroil .... ferrous sulphate
ironstone .... limonite
isinglass .... fish glue & ichthyocolla
isinglass, japanese .... agar agar
isopropanol .... isopropyl alchol
italian red .... iron oxide
ivory black .... bone black
japan earth .... cutch
japan fish oil .... sardine oil
japan isinglass .... agar
japan tallow .... japan wax
japan wax .... light yellow cakes
jaune de mars .... iron oxide, yellow
javell water .... potassium hypochlorite solution
javelle water .... sodium hypochlorite
jelutong .... gum pontianak
jesuit's balsam .... copaiba balsam
jesuits bark .... cinchona
jew's pitch .... asphaltum
jeweler's putty .... oxide of tin
jeweller's red .... ferric oxide
jeweller's rouge .... ferric oxide
juniper gum .... gum sandarac
kadaya .... gum karaya
kaiser green .... copper acetoarsenite
kalium .... potassium
kalsomine .... zinc oxide, whitewash
kanten .... agar agar
kaolin .... china clay

katchung oil .... peanut oil
katechu .... cutch
kauri gum .... copal gum
kermes mineral .... antimony pentasulphide
kierserite .... magnesium sulphate
kieselguhr .... infusorial earth, tripoli, diatomaceous earth
killeen .... irish moss
king's blue .... cobalt blue & smalt
king's green .... copper acetoarsenite
king's yellow .... arsenic sulphide, arsenic trisulphide
kobelt .... arsenical cobalt sulphide, cadmia, calamine
kohl .... antimony sulphide, galena
kryolith .... cryolite
kupfernickel .... niccolite (nickel arsenide)
labarraque's solution .... javelle water
lac .... shellac
lac sulphur .... precipitated sulphur
lactate of iron .... ferrous lactate
lactin .... lactose
lake .... lac resin
laminated talc .... mica
lamp black .... carbon black
lanolin .... adeps lanae
lanum .... lanolin
lapis caustic .... silver nitrate
lapis infernalis .... fused nitrate of silver
latent heat .... caloric
latex .... liquid rubber
latic acid .... alphahydroxypropionic acid
latten .... a brass alloy
laudanum .... tincture of opium
laughing gas .... nitrous oxide
layor-carang .... agar
lead acetate .... plumbic acetate; sugar of lead
lead antimoniate .... antimony yellow
lead carbonate .... cerussite; flake white
lead chromate .... chrome yellow, paris yellow
lead diacetate .... lead acetate
lead dichromate .... chrome orange; chrome red
lead flake .... lead, white
lead glass .... flint glass
lead monoxide .... lead oxide
lead ochre .... lead oxide
lead oxide .... litharge; massicot; scale litharge
lead oxide, red .... minium, red lead, plumbic oxide
lead subacetate .... tribasic lead acetate
lead sulfate, basic .... whitelead, sublimed
lead sulphate, basic .... plumbous sulphate
lead tungstate .... wolframate, raspite
lead, white .... ceruse, lead subcarbonate

leaf green .... chlorophyll
leather grease .... degras
lees .... dregs
leiccom .... dextrin
leipsig yellow .... lead chromate
lemnos earth .... red iron oxide
lemon chrome .... barium chromate
lemon yellow .... lead chromate
lemon, salts of .... potassium binoxalate
lencogen .... sodium bisulphite
leopard's bane .... arnica
ley .... caustic soda
leyden blue .... cobalt blue
leys .... solutions of alkalies
libavius' fuming liquor .... stannic chloride
licorice .... glycyrrhiza
light hydrochloric ether .... ethyl chloride
light carburetted hydrogen .... methane
light ligroin .... petroleum ether
lignite wax .... monton wax
ligroin .... petroleum ether
lime .... calcium oxide, quick lime, burnt lime, calx
lime hydrate .... calcium hydroxide & slaked lime
lime nitrogen .... calcium cyanamide
lime pyrolignite .... calcium acetate
lime saltpeter .... calcium nitrate
lime sulphur............................ liver of lime, calcic liver of sulphur
lime water .... calcium hydroxide solution
lime, slaked .... calcium hydroxide
lime, unslaked .... calcium oxide
limestone .... calcium carbonate
limonite .... hydrous iron oxide
linen seed oil .... linseed oil
linseed .... flaxseed
linum .... flaxseed
liquid ammonia .... ammonia, anhydrous
liquid bitumen.. petroleum
liquid camphor .... camphor oil
liquid glass .... potassium silicate, sodium silicate
liquid paraffin.. mineral oil
liquid pitch oil .... creosote oil
liquid rubber .... latex
liquid silex................................ sodium or potassium silicate
liquid soaps .... potash soaps
liquor calcis.................................. solution of lime, lime water
liquor of flints.................................. solutions of siliceous potash
liquor silicum .... solutions of siliceous potash
lissamine fast yellow .... yellow dye
litharge................................. lead monoxide, lead oxide,
.... semi-vitreous oxide of lead, yellow lead oxide

lithii benzoas .... lithium benzoate
lithium .... silver gray metal
lithopone .... white zinc pigment,
.... zinc sulphide & barium sulphate mix
liver of lime .... lime sulphur
liver of sulphur .... potassium sulphide
liver of sulphur, alkaline .... sulphuret of potash
liver of sulphur, calcareous .... sulphuret of lime
liver ore .... red mercury sulphide
liver-colored silver .... silver bromide
loccu oil .... olive oil
lodestone .... magnetite, iron oxide
logwood .... haematoxylum
lugal solution .... potassium iodide
lumar caustic .... silver nitrate
luna cornea .... muriate of silver
lunar caustic .... silver nitrate
lye .... caustic soda, sodium or potassium hydroxide
lyztmose .... litmus
macis .... mace
madder .... gamene
magistery of bismuth .... oxide of bismuth by the nitric acid
magistery of lead .... precipitated oxide of lead
magnate of baryta .... barium manganate
magnes carneus .... white earth
magnesia .... calcined magnesia, magnesium oxide,
.... hydrated magnesium carbonate,
.... lodestone, talc (magnesium silicate)
magnesia aerated .... carbonate of magnesia
magnesia alba .... carbonate of magnesia, magnesium oxide
magnesia black .... black oxide of manganese
magnesian limestone .... dolomite
magnesite .... magnesium carbonate
magnesite cement .... calcined magnesite
magnesium .... manganese
magnesium aluminate .... spinel
magnesium carbonate .... magnesia alba
magnesium hydroxide .... magnesium hydrate & brucite
magnesium oxide .... calcined magnesia; perclastite
magnesium powder .... silver colored metal
magnesium silicate .... talcum
magnesium stearate .... dolomol
magnesium sulphate .... bitter purging salt
magnesium, calcined .... magnesium oxide
magnetite .... lodestone (ferric oxide)
maize oil .... corn oil
malachite, artifical .... copper carbonate
malayan camphor .... borneol
malic acid .... maleinic acid, apple acid
malt sugar .... maltose

28

manganese dioxide .... black oxide of manganese
manganese peroxide .... manganese dioxide
mangani dioxidum .... black oxide of manganese
manganic acid .... permanganic acid
maquers salt .... potassium arsenate
maranata .... corn starch & arrowroot
marble .... calcium carbonate
marble dust .... calcium carbonate
marbon white .... lithopone
marine acid .... hydrochloric acid
marine glue .... waterproof glue
marine salt .... sodium chloride
mars red .... red iron oxide
mars yellow .... iron oxide, yellow
marsh gas .... methane
massicot .... lead oxide
massicot, masticot .... lead ochre (lead oxide)
mastic gum .... gum mastic
masticot .... yellow oxide of lead
masurium .... technetium
matrass .... cucurbit
matricaria .... german chamomile
matter of heat .... caloric
matter, amylacious .... fecula, or starch
mayence .... strass
meadow green .... copper acetoarsenite
mecca galls .... nutgalls
meerschaum .... serpentine
melaconite .... cupric oxide
menaccin .... titanium
menesc .... madder
menhaden oil .... pogy oil & mossbunker oil
mephitic air .... nitrogen
mephitis .... nitrogen
mercuric chloride .... corrosive sublimate
mercuric nitrate .... pernitrate of mercury
mercuric oxide .... red mercuric oxide
mercurium calcinatus .... mercuric oxide
mercurius vitae .... antimony oxychloride
mercurous chloride .... calomel
mercurous oxide .... black precipitate
mercurous sulphate .... turpeth mineral
mercury .... quicksilver; silvery liquid
mercury bichloride .... corrosive sublimate
mercury chloride .... mercurous chloride
mercury sulphide, red .... vermillion chinese vermillion
metallic arsenic .... pure arsenic
methanol .... wood alcohol, methyl alcohol
methyl benzoate .... oil of niobe or essence of niobe
methyl cellosolve .... ethylene glycol monomethyl ether

29

methyl chloride .... chloromethane
methylated spirits .... methyl alcohol
methylphenyl ether .... anisol, anisiole
metol .... methyl-paraaminophenol sulphate
metso crystals .... sodium metasilicate
mexico seed .... castor bean
mica .... muscovite, laminated talc
microcosmic salt .... sodium ammonium phosphate
milk of magnesia .... magnesium hydroxide in water
milk sugar .... lactose
mimosa bark .... wattle bark
mineral black .... slate black
mineral butter .... antimony chloride
mineral carbon .... graphite
mineral fat .... petrolatum
mineral green .... copper arsenite & copper carbonate
mineral hamburg .... copper carbonate, blue
mineral oil .... liquid paraffin, colorless liquid
mineral pitch .... asphalt
mineral wax .... ozokerite & cersin wax
minium .... lead oxide, red oxide of lead,
.... vermilion, cinnabar, litharge
mirabilite .... glauber's salt
mirbane oil .... nitrobenzene, nitrobenzol
mischmetall .... mixture of iron and rare-earth metals (lighter flints)
mispickel .... arsenopyrite (iron arsenic sulphide)
misture cretæ .... chalk mixture
misy .... ochre containing iron sulphate
mitcham .... oil of lavender
mitis green .... copper acetoarsentie
mittler's green .... guignet green
mofette .... nitrogen
mohr's salt .... ferrous ammonium sulphate
moldex .... preservative
molybdaena .... lead ore (lead carbonate), litharge
molybdaenum ..... graphite, molybdenite (molybdenum disulphide)
molybdena .... galenite, galena (lead sulphide)
monks hood .... aconite
monoammoniac carbonate .... ammonium bicarbonate
monosodium phosphate .... sodium phosphate
montan wax .... lignite wax
mordant salt .... aluminum acetate, basic
morphinæ .... morphine, alkaloid of opium
morrhua oil .... cod liver oil
mosaic gold .... tin bisulphide
moschus .... musk from preputial follicles of ox
moss green .... copper acetoarsenite
mossbunker's oil .... menhaden oil
mother waters .... deliquescent saline residues
mountain verditer .... copper carbonate, blue

mucilago .... mucilage of various gums & extract
murexide .... purpuriate of ammonium muriate
muriate .... chloride
muriatic acid .... hydrochloric acid
muriatic ether .... ethyl chloride
murillo bark .... soap bark
muscovite .... mica
myrobalan extract .... hurr nuts & terminala chebula
myrtle wax .... bayberry wax
naphtha, solvent .... coal tar naphtha
naphthalene .... coal tar solvent
naphthalenum .... hydrocarbon from coal tar
naphthenic acid .... hexahydrobenxoic acid
naphthol .... phenol or alcohol from coal tar
naples yellow .... lead antimoniate
naptha .... petroleum solvent
natrium .... sodium
natron, nitron, nitrum .... soda, sodium carbonate, potash
natrum .... sodium
natural gas .... mostly methane
neetsfoot oil .... hoofoil, oil bubulum
nervine balsam .... baume nerval
nevin'swhite .... lithopone
new green .... copper acetoarsenite
nickel .... steel gray metal
nickel black .... nickel oxide
nickel oxide .... nickel peroxide
nickel salt, single................................... nickel sulphate
nickel salts, double............................ nickel ammonium sulphate
nickel sulphate .... single nickel salts
nickel-silver..................................... copper-nickel alloy
nickelic oxide .... nickel peroxide
nicotine .... alkaloid from tobacco
niter, ... potassium nitrate
niter cake, nitre cake .... sodium bisulphate
nitre .... nitrate of potash
nitres .... nitrates
nitric acid .... mineral acid
nitrobenzene .... oil mirbane, nitrobenzol
nitrocellulose...................... gun cotton, pyroxylin
nitrolin .... calcium cyanamide
nitrous air .... nitric oxide
norwegian saltpeter .... calcium nitrate
nostrum .... patent medicine
nuremburg red .... red iron oxide
nushadur .... ammonium carbonate
nut oil .... china wood oil
nutgalls .... used in manufacture of black ink
nux vomica........................... brucine, strychnia alkaloid
ochres .... iron oxides yellow to red

octadecadienoic acid .... linoleic acid
octadecanoic acid .... stearic acid
oil of almonds, artificial .... benzaldhyde
oil of ants, artificial .... furfural
oil of bitumen .... petroleum
oil of cassia .... oil of cinnamon
oil of dippel .... oil distilled from bones
oil of mirrane .... nitrobenzene
oil of niobe .... methyl benzoate
oil of vitriol .... sulphuric acid
oil of wintergreen .... methyl salicylate
oille of tartre .... cream of tartar
oils of tartar per deliquium .... solution of carbonate of potash
oils, essential .... volatile oils
oils, etheral .... volatile oils
oils, fat .... fixed oils
oleatum .... acid oil from fats
oleic acid .... elaic acid; red oil, soluble in ether
olein .... glyceryl tri-oleate
oleine .... turkey red oil
oleoresina .... resin oils
oleum .... fixed or volatile oils, oil of tar,
.... sulphuric acid, pyrosulphuric acid
oleum adipis .... fixed oil expressed from lard
oleum olivae .... olive oil
olive oil .... sweet oil
opal wax .... synthetic wax
opii pulvis .... powdered opium
orange cadmium... cadmium sulphide
orange metal .... form of red lead
orange mineral .... orange red lead oxide
orchil .... archil, cudbear
orichalcum, aurichalcum....................................... brass, bronze
orient yellow .... cadmium sulphide
origanum .... sweet marjoram
orleana .... annatto
ormulu .... brass of color of gold
orpimen, orpiment................................yellow arsenic trisulphide
orpiment .... arsenic trisulphide, arsenous sulphide (yellow)
orr's white .... lithopone
orseille .... cudbear & orchil extract
orthophosphoric acid .... phosphoric acid
oxalate .... salt of oxalic acid
oxalic acid .... organic acid
oxone .... sodium peroxide
oxygenated water... hydrogen peroxide
oxymethylene .... formaldehyde
oxymuriate acid .... hypochlorous acid
oxymuriate of lime .... calcium hypochlorite
oxymuriate of mercury .... mercuric chloride

oxymuriatic acid gas .... chlorine
oxysulphuret of antimony .... antimony pentasulphide
ozokerite wax .... mineral wax, fossil wax
pale catechu .... gum gambier
pale oxide of iron .... red iron oxide
palladium .... silver white metal
palm butter .... palm oil
palm wax .... yellowish mass
palmitic acid .... ethalic acid
panama bark .... soap bark
panchromium .... vanadium
papermaker's alum .... aluminum sulphate
paraffin oil .... mineral oil, petrolatium
paraffin wax .... wax from petroleum
paraformaldehyde .... white powder w/odor of formaldehyde
paramalic acid .... fumaric acid
pariffin oil .... oil from petroleum
paris blue .... ferrocyanic acid
paris green .... copper acetoarsenite, copper arsenite
paris white .... calcium carbonate, whiting
paris yellow .... lead chromate
parrote green .... copper acetoarsenite
patent alum .... aluminum sulphate
patent red .... red mercury sulphide
patgreen .... copper acetoarsenite
peanut oil .... arachis oil
pear oil .... amyl acetate
pearl alum .... aluminum sulphate
pearl ash .... potassium carbonate
pearl moss .... irish moss
pearl white .... bismuth oxychloride, bismuth subnitrate
pearlash lye .... potassium carbonate
pearly salt .... sodium phosphate
pelargonic ether .... oenanthic ether
pellitory root .... pyrethrum
pepsinum saccharatum .... sugared pepsin, 9 to1
perborax .... sodium perborate
perchloride of gold .... auric chloride
perchloride of iron .... ferric chloride
perchloride of manganese .... manganese perchloride
perchloride of mercury .... mercuric chloride
perchloride of potassa .... potassium perchlorate
perchloride of tin .... stannic chloride
periclasite .... magnesium oxide
perlate salt .... sodium phosphate
permanent alkali .... soda, potash
permanganic acid .... manganic acid
permanganic oxide .... manganese dioxide
peroxide .... hydrogen peroxide
persalt of iron .... ferric sulphate

persian red .... red iron oxide
persio .... cudbear
persulphate of iron .... ferrous sulphate
peruvian bark .... cinchona
peruvian niter .... sodium nitrate
petalite .... lithium aluminum silicate
petrol .... gasoline
petrolatum .... petroleum jelly
petrolatum liquidum .... liquid petroleum
petroleum ether .... canadol, used as a solvent
phenic acid .... phenol
phenol .... carbolic acid
phenol hydride .... benzene
phenylamine .... aniline
phenylethane .... ethyl benzene
phlogiston .... hypothetical fluid once used to explain combustion
phosgene .... carbonyl chloride
phosphate of baryta .... barium phosphate
phosphate of iron .... ferric phosphate
phosphate of lime .... calcium phosphate
phosphate of manganese .... manganous phosphate
phosphine .... phosphorus trihydride
phosphoretted hydrogen .... phosphoric acid
phosphoric acid .... orthophosphoric acid
phosphoric salts .... phosphates
physostigma .... calabar bean
pickle alum .... aluminum sulphate
picric acid .... trinitrophenol
pilocarpus .... jaborandi
pimenta .... allsprice
pineapple oil .... ethyl butyrate
pinolith .... lithopone
pipe clay .... china clay
pistachia galls .... gum mastic
pitch, burgundy .... resin from european pine
pitch, coke .... carbon, black solid fuel
pitch, pine .... prime pitch, shoemakers wax
pitchblende .... uranium oxide
pix burgundica .... resin of burgundy pine
pix liquida .... pine tar
plaster of paris .... calcium sulphate, gypsum
platina mohr .... platinum black
plessy's green .... chromium phosphate
plumbago .... graphite, hyper-carburet of iron
plumbate of oxide of lead .... red lead oxide
plumbate of soda .... red lead oxide in sodium hydroxide
plumbi acetas .... lead acetate, sugar of lead
plumbic acetate .... lead acetate
plumbic oxide .... red lead oxide
plumbum .... tin, lead

34

plumbum argentum .... pewter
plumbum candium, candidum .... tin
plumbum nigrum .... lead
pluranium .... ruthenium
podophyllum .... roots of may apple
pogy oil .... menhaden oil
poke root, weed .... hellebore
polisher's putty .... stannic oxide
polishing crocus .... red iron oxide
pompholyx .... zinc oxide plus arsenic oxide
ponderous magnesia .... magnesium oxide
pontianak gum .... gum pontianak
porcelain clay .... china clay
porcelain white .... lithopone
porous alum .... sodium alum
potash .... potassium carbonate
potash alum .... alum, alum flowers, alum meal
potash chrome alum .... chromium potassium sulphate
potash of commerce .... potassium carbonate
potash water .... potassium hydroxide in solution
potash water glass .... potassium silicate
potash, caustic .... potassium hydroxide
potassa .... potassium hydroxide
potassa cum calce .... potassa with lime
potassa hydrate .... potassium hydrate
potassa sulphurata .... lime of sulphur
potassii acetas .... potassium acetate
potassii bitartras .... cream of tartar
potassii et sodii tartras .... rochelle salts
potassii nitras .... saltpetre
potassium .... kalium
potassium acetate .... diuretic salt; potassic acetate
potassium acid oxalate .... potassium binoxalate
potassium acid tartrate .... potassum bitartrate
potassium bicarbonate .... salaterus
potassium bichromate .... potassium dichromate
potassium binoxalate .... potassium acid oxalate,
.... potassium hydrogen oxalate
potassium bisulphate .... potassium acid sulphate
potassium chlorate .... potassium oxymuriate
potassium chromate .... yellow crystals for use in dyes
potassium dichromate .... potassium bichromate
potassium ferricyanide .... red prussiate of potash
potassium ferrocyanide .... yellow prussiate of potash
potassium hydrate .... potassium hydroxide
potassium hydroxide .... caustic potash
potassium iodide .... lugal solution, potassic iodine
potassium laurate .... tan colored paste
potassium linoleate .... tan paste; emulsifying agent
potassium muriate .... potassium chloride

35

potassium nitrate .... niter and saltpeter
potassium persulphate .... anthron
potassium rhodanide .... potassium sulphocyanide
potassium silicate .... potash water-glass
potassium sulphate .... salt of lemery
potassium sulphocyanide .... potassium rhodanide
potassium tartrate .... sal vegetal
potato oil .... fusel oil
potato starch .... starch
powder of algaroth .... antimony oxychloride
prague red sinopis .... red iron oxide
precipitate per se .... red oxide of mercury by fire
precipitate, red .... red oxide of mercury by the nitric acid
precipitated chalk .... calcium carbonate
preservaline .... formaldehyde
preston salts .... ammonium sesquicarbonate
principle, acidifying .... oxygen
principle, astringent .... gallic acid
principle, inflammable .... phlogiston
principle, tanning .... tannin
protocarbonate of iron .... ferrous carbonate
protochloride iron .... ferrous chloride
protochloride of gold .... aurous chloride
protochloride of mercury .... mercurous chloride
prussian blue .... ferric ferrocyanide, chinese blue,
.... hydrocyanic acid, prussiate of iron
prussiate of copper .... copper ferrocyanide
prussiate of iron .... ferric cyanide
prussiate of mercury .... mercuric cyanide
prussiate of potash .... potassium ferrocyanide
prussiate of potash, red .... potassium ferricyanide
prussiate of potash, yellow .... potassium ferrocyanide
prussiate of soda .... sodium ferrocyanide
prussic acid .... hydrocyanic acid
psyllium seed .... fleaseed and fleawort
pulp oil .... aluminum acetate, basic
pumex .... pumice stone
purified ozokerite .... ceresin wax
purple oxide .... red iron oxide
purpurate of ammonia .... murexide of ammonia
pyramidon .... amidopyrine
pyrethrum .... insect flowers
pyrites .... ferrous sulphide, galena, or any metallic sulphide
pyrites factitious .... sulphuret of iron
pyrites of copper .... sulphuret of copper
pyrites of martial .... sulphuret of iron
pyrites of silver .... siderite
pyro .... pyrogallic acid
pyroborate .... sodium borate
pyrocatechol .... catechol and oxyphenic acid

36

pyrogallic acid .... pyrogallol and trihydroxybenzene
pyrogallol .... pyrogallic acid
pyroligneous acid .... acetic acid, wood vinegar
pyroligneous ether .... ethyl acetate
pyrolignite of iron .... protoacetate of iron
pyrolusite .... manganese dioxide
pyromucic aldehyde .... furfural
pyrophosphate of soda .... sodium pyrophosphate
pyrosulphuric acid .... fuming sulphuric acid
pyroxylin scrap .... celluloid scrap
pyroxylin solutions .... collodion
pyroxylinum .... soluble gun cotton
qalqand .... green vitriol, iron sulphate
quadrisilicate .... sodium silicate
quadroxalate of potassa .... potassium acid oxalate
quartz .... silica
quercetin .... quercitron extract
quercitron .... quercitin, a tanning substance
quicklime .... calcium oxide, lime
quicksilver .... mercury
quicksilver vermilion .... red mercury sulphide
quillaia .... soap bark
raddle .... red iron oxide
radical vinegar .... acetic acid
ramie .... china grass
rape oil .... rapeseed oil
raspite .... lead tungstate
ratsbane .... white arsenic, arsenic trioxide
realgar .... arsenic disulphide, red arsenic
rectified tar .... tar oil
red argols .... argols
red arsenic .... arsenic disulphide
red bole .... ferric oxide, red iron oxide
red chalk .... red iron oxide
red gum .... gum accroides
red lake .... lac resin
red lead .... lead oxide
red liquor .... aluminum acetate, basic
red mercuric sulphuret .... red mercury sulphide
red ochre .... red iron oxide
red oil .... oleic acid
red orpiment .... red arsenic
red oxide .... red ferric oxide
red oxide of copper .... cuprous oxide
red oxide of mercury .... mercuric oxide
red peruvian bark .... cinchona
red precipitate .... mercuric oxide
red prussiate .... potassium ferricyanide
red prussiate of potash .... potassium ferricyanide
red prussiate of soda .... sodium ferricyanide

red sanders .... red sandalwood
red silver .... pyragyrite (silver antimony sulphide)
reddle ....red iron oxide
regulus of metal .... metal in a state of purity
resin copal .... gum copal
resin damar... gum damar
retinol .... rosin oil
reulgar .... red sulphuretted oxide of arsenic
rhamnus ....vervain
rhus glabbra ....sumac
rice starch .... starch
ricinus .... castor bean
ricinus oil .... castor oil
roasted copper............................artificial copper oxide or sulphide
rochelle salt..................................... potassium & sodium tartrate,
.... potassium sodium tartrate
rock oil .... petroleum
rock salt .... sodium chloride
rock salt moss .... irish moss
roman vitriol .... cupric sulphate
rosin .... colophony, abietic anhydride
rosin oil .... codoil,retinol
ross' white .... lithopone
rotenone...insecticide
rottenstone .. decomposed siliceous limestone , terra cariosa, tripoli
roucon .... annatto
rouge.. ferric oxide
rouge de mars ....red iron oxide
rubigo ....red iron oxide
ruby copper .... cuprite (copper pyrite)
ruby silver .... proustite (silver arsenic sulphide)
rudis copper .... chalcocite (copper ore), copper glance
rudis silver .... silver ore (sulphide, chloride, arsenide)
rust of copper .... green oxide of copper
rust of iron .... oxide of iron
rutile .... titanium oxide
saccharine.. glucoside
saffron of mars .... red oxide of iron
sago acetosella .... potassium binoxalate
sago dextrin .... dextrin
sal ammonia... ammonium chloride
sal ammoniac .... ammonium chloride, muriate of ammonia
sal armoniack.. sal ammoniac
sal catharticum ....magnesium sulphate
sal chalybis .... ferrous sulphate
sal culinaris .... sodium chloride
sal mirabile .... glauber's salt
sal polychrest .... potassium sulphate
sal soda.. crystalline sodium carbonate,
.... unrefined sodium carbonate

sal tartari .... potassium carbonate
sal vegetol .... potassium tartrate
sal volatile ..... ammonium carbonate, ammonium sesquicarbonate
salad oil .... cottonseed oil
saleratus .... potassium bicarbonate, sodium bicarbonate
salicylic acid .... orthohydroxybenzoic acid
salmiac .... ammonium chloride
salt–glass .... melted sodium chloride
salt .... sodium chloride
salt cake .... sodium sulphate
salt green .... copper acetate and chloride
salt of amber .... succinic acid
salt of ammon .... sal ammoniac
salt of barilla .... sodium carbonate
salt of benzoin .... benzoic acid
salt of chrome .... potassium chromate
salt of colcothar .... ferrous sulphate
salt of hartshorn .... ammonium carbonate
salt of lemery .... potassium sulphate
salt of lemon .... potassium binoxalate
salt of satum .... lead acetate
salt of seignette .... sodium potassium tartrate
salt of soda .... sodium carbonate
salt of sorrel .... potassium binoxalate, potassium quadroxalate
salt of steel .... ferrous sulphate
salt of tartar .... cream of tartar
salt of tartar .... potassium carbonate
salt of vitroil .... zinc sulphate
salt of wormwood .... potassium carbonate
salt, sedative .... boracic acid
salt, sthal's sulphurous .... sulphate of potash
salt, common .... sodium chloride
salt, common or sea .... muriate of soda
salt, febrifuge of silvius .... muriate of potass
salt, fusible of urine .... phosphate of soda and ammonia
salt, vegetable .... tartrate of potass
saltpeter .... potassium nitrate
saltpeter chile .... sodium nitrate
saltpeter paper .... touch paper
saltpeter, nitre .... potassium nitrate
saltpetre .... nitrate of potash, potassium nitrate
salts of tartar .... potassium carbonate
salts of vitroil .... zinc sulphate
salts of wormwood .... potassium carbonate
salufer .... sodium silicofluoride
salzburg vitriol .... copper sulphate
sand acid .... hydrofluosilic acid
sandalwood oil .... santalum album
sandarac .... realgar
sandarac gum .... gum sandarac

39

sanguis draconis (dragon's blood) .... red resin
santalum album .... sandalwood oil
santonate of soda .... sodium santonate
sapo .... soap, soda & olive oil
sarcocolla .... Ethiopian resin
sardine oil .... japan fish oil
satin spar .... gypsum and satin white
saturnus .... lead
saxoline .... petrolatum
saxony blue .... smalt
scale wax .... paraffin wax
scheele's green .... copper arsenite
schlippe's salt .... antimony pentasulphide
schweinfurth green .... copper acetoarsenite
sea salt .... sodium chloride
seed oil .... cottonseed oil
seignette's salt .... sodium & potassium tartrate
selenite .... calcium sulphate, gypsum
seolfor .... silver
sepia .... cuttlefish ink
septic acid .... nitric acid
septon .... nitrogen
sericose .... cellulose acetate
serpentine .... asbestos
sesame oil .... gigely oil, teel or til oil
sesquicarbonate of ammonia .... ammonium sesquicarbonate
sesquicarbonate of soda .... sodium sesquicarbonate
sesquicupric carbonate .... copper carbonate, blue
sevum .... mutton suet
shark liver oil .... shark oil
shellac .... lac, mecca, garnet lac
shoemakers black .... ferrous sulphate
siberian red lead .... crucoite (lead chromate)
siderite .... ferrous carbonate, iron carbonate ore, lodestone
silica .... silex, silicon dioxide, quartz
silicate of soda .... water glass
silicium, silicum .... silicon
silicon dioxide .... silica
silk oil .... textile oils
silver .... argentum
silver glance .... silver sulphide
silver nitrate .... lunar caustic
sinapis alba .... white mustard
sinapis nigra .... black mustard
slaked lime .... calcium hydroxide, lime hydrate
slate black .... mineral black
smalt .... saxony blue, king's blue
smaltine .... powdered blue glass pigment
smelling salts .... ammonium sesquicarbonate
smithsonite .... zinc carbonate

snowflake crystals .... sodium sesquicarbonate
soap bark ....china bark, panama bark
soap, castile .... olive oil soap
soapstone .... impure magnesium sulphate, talc
sod oil ....degras
soda .... sodium carbonate or hydroxide
soda alum .... sodium alum
soda ash.. sodium carbonate
soda crystals .... sodium carbonate
soda glass .... common glass
soda lime............................... sodium hydroxide & calcium oxide
soda nitre saliter .... sodium nitrate
soda, caustic .... sodium hydroxide
sodic hydrate... sodium hydroxide
sodii acetas .... soda & acetic acid
sodii arsenas .... soda & arsenic
sodii benzoas.. benzoate of soda
sodii bicarbonas .... bicarbonate of soda
sodii chloridum .... salt
sodii sulphas .... glauber's salt
sodium .... natrium
sodium alum .... aluminum sodium sulphate
sodium bicarbonate .... baking soda
sodium bichromate... sodium dichromate
sodium bisulphate............. nitre, niter cake; sodium acid sulphate
sodium bisulphite........................ lencogen, sodium acid sulphite,
.... sodium acid sulphate
sodium borate ....borax; sodium tetraborate
sodium carbonate ....cyrstals carbonate
sodium choleate .... extract of ox gall
sodium ferricyanide ....red prussiate of soda
sodium ferrocyanide .... yellow prussiate of soda
sodium fluoride ....fluorol
sodium hydrosulphite.................. hydrosulphite - bleaching agent
sodium hydroxide ....caustic soda
sodium hypochlorite ....javelle water
sodium lauryl sulphate............. sulphated alcohol - soap substitute
sodium nitrate............................... chile saltpetre, chilian saltpeter
sodium oleate .... eunatrol
sodium perborate .... perborin, perborax
sodium phosphate ....disodic orthophosphate, disodium phosphate
sodium phosphate, dibasic .... disodium phosphate
sodium phosphate, monobasic .... monosodium phosphate
sodium phosphate, tribasic .... trisodium phosphate
sodium sesquicarbonate .... snowflake crystals
sodium silicate ....soda glass, water glass
sodium silicofluoride .... salufer, sodium fluosilicate
sodium sulphate.. salt cake
sodium sulphide... sodium sulfuret
sodium sulphocyanate............................... sodium sulphocyanide

41

sodium tetraborate .... sodium borate
sodium thiosulphate .... hypo
soja bean oil .... soya bean oil
sol .... gold
solid bitumen .... asphalt
soluble glass .... sodium silicate
soluble oil .... sulphonated oil
solvative water .... nitric acid
sory .... a stone containing copper and iron
spanish green .... basic copper acetate
spanish oxide .... red iron oxide
spanish white .... bismuth subnitrate
spanish whiting .... calcium carbonate
spar, calcarious .... crystallized carbonate of lime
spar, fluor .... fluorate of lime
spar, ponderous .... sulphate of barytes
spathic iron ore .... ferrous carbonate
spelter .... zinc
spermaceti .... cetaceum, wax from sperm whale
sphalerite .... zinc sulphide
spinel .... magnesium aluminate
spirit of hartshorn .... ammonia
spirit of nitre .... nitric acid
spirit of nitre, fuming .... nitrous acid
spirit of sal .... muriatic acid
spirit of sal ammoniac .... ammonia
spirit of salt .... hydrochloric acid
spirit of salts .... hydrochloric acid
spirit of vitriol .... sulphuric acid
spirit of wine .... alcohol
spirit, ardent .... alcohol
spirits .... distilled ethyl alcohol
spirits of hartshorn .... ammonia, solution of
spirits of turpentine .... turpentine
spiritus ferri chloridi .... chloride of iron
spiritus fumans .... tin chloride
spiritus hyoscyami .... henbane
spiritus iodi .... metallic element from seaweed
spiritus menthæ viridis .... essence of spearmint
spiritus myrciæ .... bay rum
spiritus myrrhæ .... myrrh
spiritus nucis vomicæ .... poison nut of India
spiritus rector .... aroma
spiritus salus .... hydrochloric acid
spodos... pompholyx
spodumene... lithium aluminum sulphate
spume of silver .... litharge
squaw vine .... partridgeberry
stannic oxide .... peroxide of tin; tin putty
stannous chloride .... tin crystals

stannum .... natural alloy of lead and silver,tin
starch gum .... dextrin, dextrine
stearic acid .... stearinic acid
stearin .... tristearin
stearine .... stearic acid, tristearin
stearophanic .... stearic acid
steatite .... talc
stellite .... alloy of tungsten, chromium, cobalt
stibium .... antimony, antimony sulphide
stibnite .... antimony sulphide
stibnite antimonite .... black antimony sulphide
stick lac .... shellac
stillingia oil .... tallow oil
stimmi .... antimony
stock lye .... potassium hydroxide
stolzite .... lead tungstate
stone blue .... azurite
storax .... styrax
strontanite .... strontium carbonate
strychnia .... alkaloid of nux vomica
styptic .... astringent
sublimate, corrosive .... corrosive muriate of mercury
succinum .... amber
sucrose .... cane sugar, beet sugar
sugar of lead .... lead acetate
sugar of milk .... lactose
sulfonated castor oil .... turkey red oil
sulphate of baryta .... barium sulphate
sulphonated fatty alcohols .... sodium alkyl sulphate
sulphonated oil .... turkey red oils
sulphonated olive oil .... soluble olive oil
sulphur .... brimstone, sulphur flour
sulphur gold .... antimony sulphide, golden
sulphur olive oil .... olive oil foots
sulphur, alkalinc liver of .... sulphuret of potass, soda, etc.
sulphur, metallic liver of ...... alkaline sulphurets containing metals
sulphurated lime .... calcium sulphide
sulphuretted hydrogen .... hydrogen sulphide
sulphuric acid .... oil of vitriol
sulphuric ether .... ether, ethyl oxide
sulphuris iodidum .... sulphur iodide
sulphuris lotum .... washed sulphur
sulphydric acid .... hyrdrogen sulphide
sulvere .... sulphur
sumac wax .... japan wax
sumatra camphor .... borneol
supertartrate of potassium .... potassium bitartrate
swedish green .... copper arsenite
sweet birch oil .... oil of wintergreen
sweet oil .... olive oil or other mild edible oil

43

sylvite .... potassium chloride
synthetic barytes .... blanc fixe
synthetic gaultheria oil .... methyl salicylate
synthetic gums .... dextrin
synthetic heavy spar.. blanc fixe
synthetic soap powder .... sodium lauryl sulphate
tabacum .... tobacco
talc... soapstone, steatite
talcum... magnesium silicate and talc
tallow .... suet, animal fat
tallow oil, tallow seed oil .... stillingia oil
tannate of iron.. ferrous tannate
tannic acid .... tannin, gallotannic acid
tanning grease... degras
tapioca dextrin .... dextrin
tar camphor .... naphthalene
tar iron.. protoacetate of iron
tar oil .... rectified tar oil and pine tar oil
tartar .... cream of tartar, super-tartrate of potass
tartar emetic .... antimony potassium tartrate, antimony tartrate
tartar vitriolated .... sulphate of potash
tartarate antimony .... antimony tartrate
tartarated iron.................................. ferric and potassium tartarte
tartaric acid... dihydroxysuccininc acid
tartars .... tartrates
tartarus.. potassium tartrate
tasteless salt .... sodium phosphate
teal oil, teel, teel oil.. sesame oil
tellurine .... diatomaceous earth
tenorite .... cupric oxide
terebinthina canadensis .... balsam or fir
terhydride of nitrogen .... ammonia
terpineol.. alpha terpineol
terpinol .... terpin
terra foliata tartari.. potash
terra japonica .... cutch
terra merita .... turmeric
terra ponderosa .... blanc fixe
terra silicea .... diatomaceous earth
tetrachlorethylene .... carbon bichloride
tetrachloride of tin... stannic chloride
tetralin .... tetrahydro naphthalene
tetrasilicate .... sodium silicate
thenardite miribilite... sodium sulphate
theobroma oil ....cacao butter
thistle saffron .... saffron, american
thus gum .... gum thus
thymol.. garden thyme
til oil .... sesame oil
tin ash .... tin peroxide

44

tin ashes .... stannic oxide
tin crystals .... stannous chloride, tin bichloride
tin oxide .... stannous oxide
tin peroxide .... stannic oxide, tin ash
tin putty .... stannic oxide
tin salt .... stannous chloride, tin tetrachloride
tin stone .... stannic oxide
tinctura cannabis indicæ .... indian hemp, weed of hashish
tinctura cantharidis .... spanish fly
tinctura capsici .... red pepper
tincture of iron .... ferrous sulphate
tinctures, spirituous .... resins dissolved in alcohol
tinkal .... borax
titanium dioxide .... titanium oxide, titanium white
tnt .... trinitrotoluene
toluene .... toluol
toluol .... toluene, methylbenzene
tombac .... dutch metal, red brass
tonke bean camphor .... coumarin
tonquin .... tonka bean
tophus .... limestone (calcium carbonate),
.... soapstone (magnesium silicate)
train oil .... whale oil
tree wax .... chinese wax
triacetin .... glycerol triacetate, glyceryl triacetate
tribasic phosphate of soda .... sodium phosphate
tricalcic phosphate .... calcium phosphate
tricalcium phosphate .... calcium phosphate, tribasic
trichlorethylene .... solvent and dry cleaner
trichloride of antimony .... antimony chloride
triformol .... parafromaldehyde
trihydroxy benzene .... pyrogallic acid
trihydroxybenzoic acid .... gallic acid
trinitrophenol .... picric acid
triplumbic tetroxide .... lead oxide, rd
tripoli .... siliceous abrasive, rottenstone
tripoli powder .... diatomaceous earth
tripolite .... diatomaceous earth & tripoli
trisnitrate of bismuth .... bismuth subnitrate
trochisei acidi tanniei .... tannic acid
trochisei ammonii chloridi .... ammonium chloride & additions
trocisei cretæ .... chalk & additions
true asphaltum .... asphalt
tung oil .... china wood oil
tungstate of lime .... calcium tungstate
tungstic acid .... wolframic acid & orthotungstic acid
tuno gum .... gum chicle
turbith mineral .... yellow oxide of mercury by sulphuric acid
turkey corn .... squirrel corn
turkey red .... red iron oxide

turkey red oil .... monopol, oleine
turmeric .... curry, curcuma
turnbull's blue .... ferrous ferricyanide
turpeth's mineral .... mercurous sulphate
tuscan red .... red iron oxide
tutty .... impure zinc oxide. pompholyx
uintahite .... gilsonite
ulmin brown .... vandyke brown
ulmus .... slippery elm
ultramarine blue .... pigment
unguentum .... 8 pts lard & 2 pts yellow wax
uranium oxide .... pitchblende
urea .... carbamide and carbonyldiamide
uroqoga .... ipecac root
urotropin .... hexamethyleneteramine
valentenite .... antimony trioxide
valerianate of amyl .... amylvaleriate
van dyke red .... red iron oxide
vaseline .... petroleum jelly
vat colors .... colors used in textile dyeing
vegetable gum .... dextrin
vegetable salt .... potassium tartrate
vegetable spermaceti .... chinese wax
vegetable tallow .... oil, vegetable
venetian red .... ferric oxide
venus crystals .... copper acetate
veratrum viride .... hellebore root
verdigris .... copper acetate, green oxide of copper
verdigris of the shops .... acetate of copper mixed with oxide
verdigris, distilled .... crystallized acetate of copper
vermifuge .... anthelmentic
vermilion .... red mercuric sulphide
vert de mitis .... copper acetoarsenite
verte emeraude .... guignet green
vichy salts .... sodium bicarbonate
vienna green .... copper acetoarsenite
vinegar .... acetic acid
vinegar acid .... acetic acid
vinegar naphtha .... ehtyl acetate
vinegar salts .... calcium acetate
vinegar, distilled .... acetous acid
vinegar, radical .... acetic acid
vini gallici .... brandy
virtrified antimony .... glass of antimony
vitellus .... yolk of egg
vitriol .... shoemaker's black, sulphuric acid
vitriol, blue .... sulphate of copper
vitriol, green .... sulphate of iron
vitriol, martial .... sulphate of iron
vitriol, roman .... sulphate of copper

vitriol, white .... sulphate of zinc
vitriolated calcareous earth ....gypsum
vitriolated tartar .... potassium sulphate
vitriolic acid...sulphuric acid
vitriols .... sulphates
vitrious silver .... silver sulphide
volatile air .... ammonia
volatile alkali .... ammonia
volatile salt................................. ammonium carbonate
wad .... hydrated manganese oxide
wali saltpeter.................................... calcium nitrate
washing soda .... sodium carbonate
water glass .... sodium silicate
water of saltpetre...................................... nitric acid
water, acidulated.............................. carbonated water
water, acreted................................... carbonated water
water, hepatic....... water impregnated with sulphuretted hydrogen
wattle bark .... mimosa bark
werk.. silver-lead alloy
westrosol .... trichlorethylene
whale oil...train oil
white vitriol .... zinc sulphate
white arsenic.......................... arsenic, arsenic trioxide
white bole .... china clay, kaolin
white caustic ....caustic soda
white chrysocolla .... borax
white copperas .... zinc sulphate
white corke.. litmus
white earth .... magnesia
white gold..platinum
white lead.................................... lead carbonate
white magnesia .... magnesium oxide
white metal .... babbitt metal
white precipitate .... mercuric ammonium chloride
white tar.. naphthalene
white vitriol .... zinc sulphate
white wax .... beeswax
white zinc ....zinc oxide
whitening .... calcium carbonate
whitewash .... calcium carbonate & sizing in water
whiting .... calcium carbonate, refined chalk, zinc oxide
whitlow .... felon
wine lees .... argols
wine of opium .... tincture of opium
wintergreen .... methyl salicylate
wintergreen oil, synthetic.................................. methyl salicylate
wismurdt... bismuth
wismuth .... bismuth
wolf bane ....aconite
wolfram .... tungsten

wolframate .... lead tungstate
wolframic acid .... tungstic acid
wonderful salt .... sodium sulphate
wood alcohol .... methanol, methyl alcohol
wood charcoal .... charcoal
wood oil .... balsam gurjun
wood spirits .... methanol
wood vinegar .... pyroligneous acid
wood's metal .... very low melting point alloy
wool fat .... adeps lanae
wool grease .... lanolin
wool mordant .... chromium sulphate
xylene .... ethyl benzene
yacca gum .... accroides gum
yellow bark .... calisaya
yellow chromate of potassa .... potassium chromate
yellow lead .... lead oxide, lead carbonate
yellow ochre .... limonite
yellow prussiate of potash .... potassium ferrocyanide
yellow prussiate of soda .... sodium ferrocyanide
yellow wax .... unbleached beeswax
zapota gum .... gum chicle
zinc bitriol .... zinc sulphate
zinc blende .... zinc sulphide
zinc chloride .... butter of chloride
zinc chromate .... zinc yellow, buttercup yellow
zinc oxide .... chinese white
zinc sulphate .... salt of vitriol
zinc sulphide .... black jack
zinc vitriol .... zinc sulphate
zinc white .... zinc oxide
zinc yellow .... potassium zinc chromate, zinc chromate
zinci acetas .... zinc acetate
zincite .... zinc oxide
zincolith .... lithopane
zincum .... zinc